WILD AND WINDY

Contents

Simon Cheshire

Story illustrated by
Martin Chatterton

In this story

 Ben

 Ruby

 Mum

 Dad

Tricky words

- leaves
- nozzle
- switched
- brilliant
- suddenly
- tornado
- reverse

Introduce these tricky words and help the reader when they come across them later!

Story starter

Ben lives with his mum and dad and his sister, Ruby. Ben loves to invent new machines. One day, he invented a wind machine to clear up the leaves in his garden.

Ben and the Wind Machine

"We have to clear up all the leaves
in the garden," said Ruby.

"No problem," said Ben. "My wind
machine will clear up the leaves."

"Your machines are rubbish!"
said Ruby.

The wind machine had a big nozzle to blow the leaves into a pile. "My machine will do the job very fast," said Ben.

Ben switched the wind machine on.
A wind blew out of the nozzle.
It blew the leaves into a pile.
"My wind machine is brilliant!"
said Ben.

But then the machine sent out sparks!

The wind suddenly blew fast.

It blew faster and faster.

The wind turned into a tornado.

The tornado blew round and round the garden. It blew around Ruby. Suddenly, it blew Ruby up into the air!

Ruby screamed and screamed.
The tornado blew her higher and
higher. She blew round and round
in the wind.

Ruby was very high up in the air.
She looked like a little dot high up
in the sky.

What will Ben
do next?

"Whoops!" said Ben. "I think the machine works too well!"

"Do something, Ben!" screamed Ruby. Ben switched the machine into reverse. The tornado went into reverse. Ruby fell down, down, down.

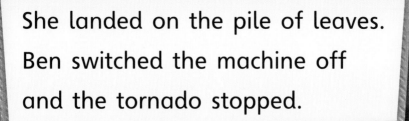

She landed on the pile of leaves.
Ben switched the machine off
and the tornado stopped.

Ruby was a mess.
Her hair was a mess.
Her dress was a mess.

Mum and Dad came into the garden.

"Who made all this mess?" they said.

"I made a wind machine to clear up the leaves," said Ben. "It blew me up into the sky," said Ruby.

"I turned the machine off and Ruby landed on the leaves," said Ben. "Nonsense!" said Dad.

"Tidy this mess or no pocket money!" said Mum.

Is Mum being fair?

"This was all your fault," said Ruby.
"Yes!" said Ben. "My wind machine
worked too well."

Quiz

Text Detective

- How did Ben stop the tornado?
- Do you think Dad believed Ben and Ruby?

Word Detective

- **Phonic Focus**: Long vowels

  Page 4: Sound out the three phonemes (sounds) in 'pile'. What long vowel can you hear?
- Page 5: Count the syllables in 'brilliant'.
- Page 11: Find a word that means the opposite of 'forward'.

Super Speller

Read these words:

worked   high   landed

Now try to spell them!

HA! HA! HA!

Q What did the bee say when it flew into the tornado?

A "Well, I'll be blowed!"

17

Find out about

- The sort of damage dangerous weather can do

Tricky words

- dangerous
- rainstorm
- damage
- hurricane
- tornado
- twisting
- hailstones
- rescued

Introduce these tricky words and help the reader when they come across them later!

Text starter

Weather can be dangerous and do a lot of damage. Storms, hurricanes, tornadoes and lightning can all kill people. Very cold or very hot weather can also be dangerous.

Dangerous Weather

Storms

A heavy rainstorm can do a lot of damage. If a lot of rain falls quickly, water can flood into people's houses.

Storms at sea

A storm at sea can do a lot of damage. The waves get higher and higher.

Some waves can be as high as a house. They can crash down on to boats and smash them on rocks.

Hurricanes

A hurricane is a huge storm. It can grow to over 100 miles wide.

Have you seen reports about hurricanes on the TV news?

Hurricanes have very strong winds. They can blow at over 200 miles an hour.

Tornado

A tornado is a tall, twisting wind.
It can be called a twister.

The wind of a tornado can blow at over 300 miles an hour. It can pick up houses, cars and people in its path.

Lightning

Lightning can do a lot of damage.
It can hit trees, houses and people.

Lightning travels at 100,000 miles a second.

Every day, about 75 people are killed by lightning.

Hailstones

Hailstones are balls of ice.
Hailstones can hit the ground at
over 100 miles an hour.
Some hailstones are small but
some hailstones can be bigger
than a cricket ball!

Cold weather

Very cold weather can be dangerous. If people get very cold, they can get ill and die. If there is a lot of snow, people can be trapped in their houses.

Some people can be trapped in their cars. They can be stuck for hours and hours. They have to be rescued.

Hot weather

Very hot weather can be dangerous.

It can set a forest on fire.

The fire burns the trees very quickly,

and it burns houses in its path.

Dangerous weather can do a lot of damage. People and animals can be killed.

Quiz

Text Detective

- Why is very cold weather dangerous?
- Have you ever seen lightning?

Word Detective

- **Phonic Focus**: Long vowels

  Page 22: Sound out the three phonemes (sounds) in 'huge'. What long vowel can you hear?
- Page 28: How many sentences on this page?
- Page 28: Find a word meaning 'caught'.

Super Speller

Read these words:

tall strong every

Now try to spell them!

HA! HA! HA!

Q What gets wet as it dries?

A A towel.